The Joy of Organ Book 2

A second book of favourite folk, popular and standard songs arranged for all organs with chord names and lyrics.
Titles include La Cumparsita, Peter and the Wolf, Beautiful Dreamer, Mexican Hat Dance.
Arranged by Kenneth Baker.

Yorktown Music Press
London/New York/Sydney/Cologne

Distributed throughout the world by Music Sales

8/9 Frith Street, London W1V 5TZ, England.

120 Rothschild Avenue, Rosebery, NSW 2018, Australia.

Printed in the United Kingdom by
J.B. Offset Printers (Marks Tey) Limited, Marks Tey, Essex.

Morning Mood
(from 'Peer Gynt')
Grieg

Electronic Organs
Upper: Oboe 8'
Lower: Flute 8'
Pedal: 8'
Vibrato: On (Medium)

Drawbar Organs
Upper: 00 3600 200
Lower: (00) 6431 100 (0)
Pedal: 4 – (2)
Vibrato: On (Medium)

In a pastoral mood ♩. = 56

Upper

Lower

Pedal

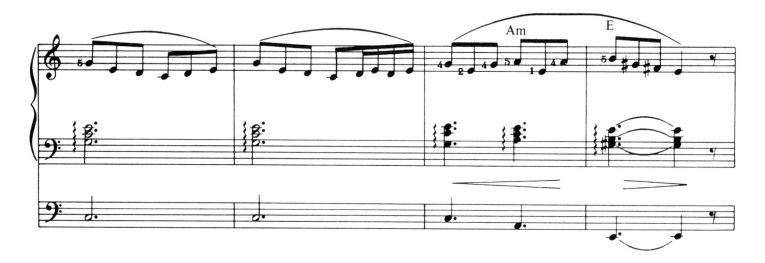

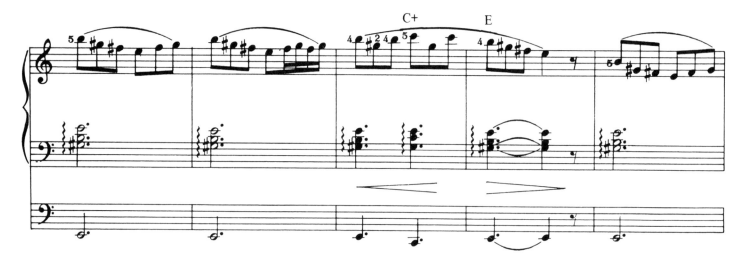

Celeste Aida

Verdi

Electronic Organs
Upper: Flute 8′, 4′
Lower: String 8′
Pedal: 8′
Vibrato: On

Drawbar Organs
Upper: 00 8008 008
Lower: (00) 5544 444 (0)
Pedal: 0 – (5)
Vibrato: On

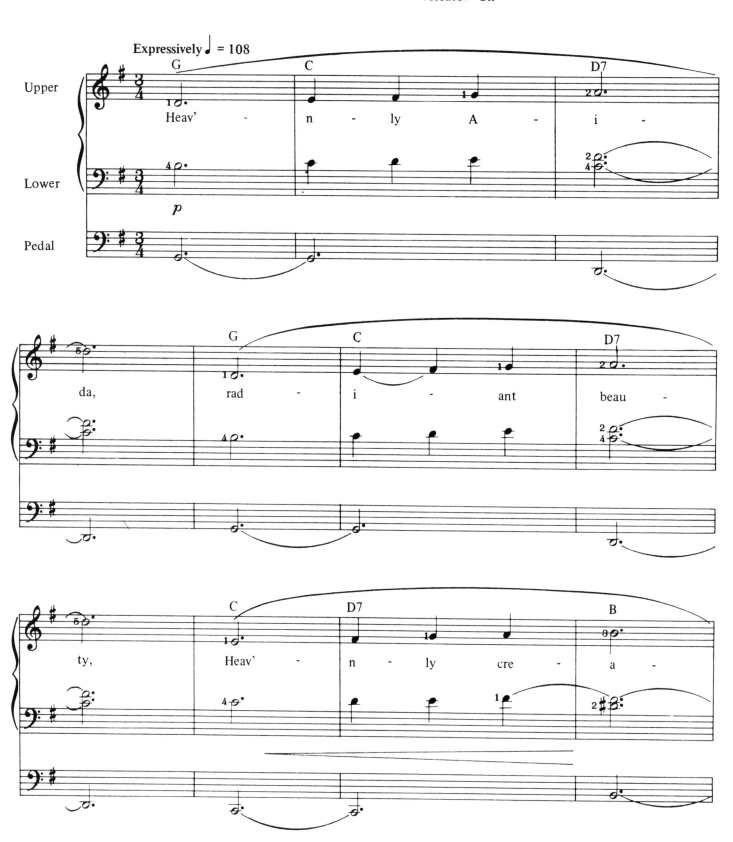

Apache Dance

Offenbach

Electronic Organs
Upper: Flute 8′, 4′
Lower: Flute 8′, String 8′
Pedal: 8′
Vibrato: On

Drawbar Organs
Upper: 00 7510 000
Lower: (00) 5443 211 (0)
Pedal: 4 – (2)
Vibrato: On

English Country Garden

Traditional

Electronic Organs
Upper: String 8′, 4′, Piano
Lower: Flute 8′, 4′
Pedal: 16′ + 8′
Vibrato: On

Drawbar Organs
Upper: 00 8757 234
Lower: (00) 7655 211 (0)
Pedal: 5 – (3)
Vibrato: On

The Washington Post March

Sousa

Electronic Organs		Drawbar Organs	
Upper:	Flute 16′, 8′, 4′, Trumpet 8′	Upper:	00 8867 420
Lower:	Flute 8′, 4′	Lower:	(00) 5655 330(0)
Pedal:	16′ + 8′	Pedal:	5 – (3)
Vibrato:	On	Vibrato:	On

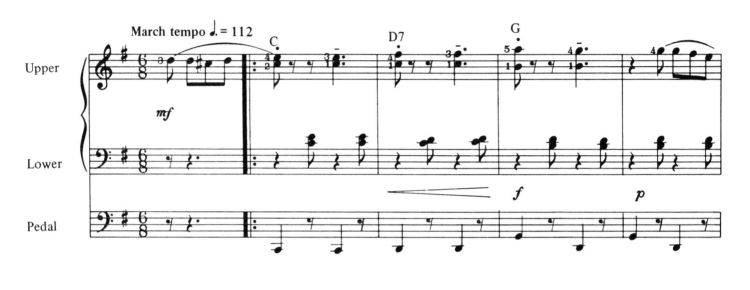

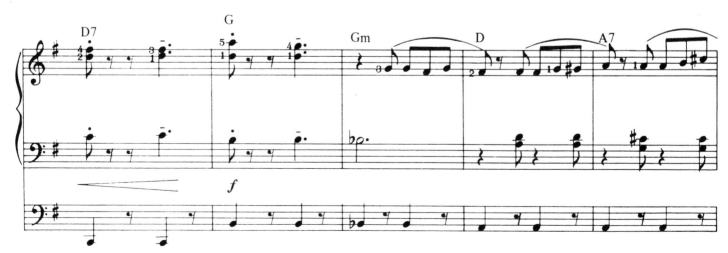

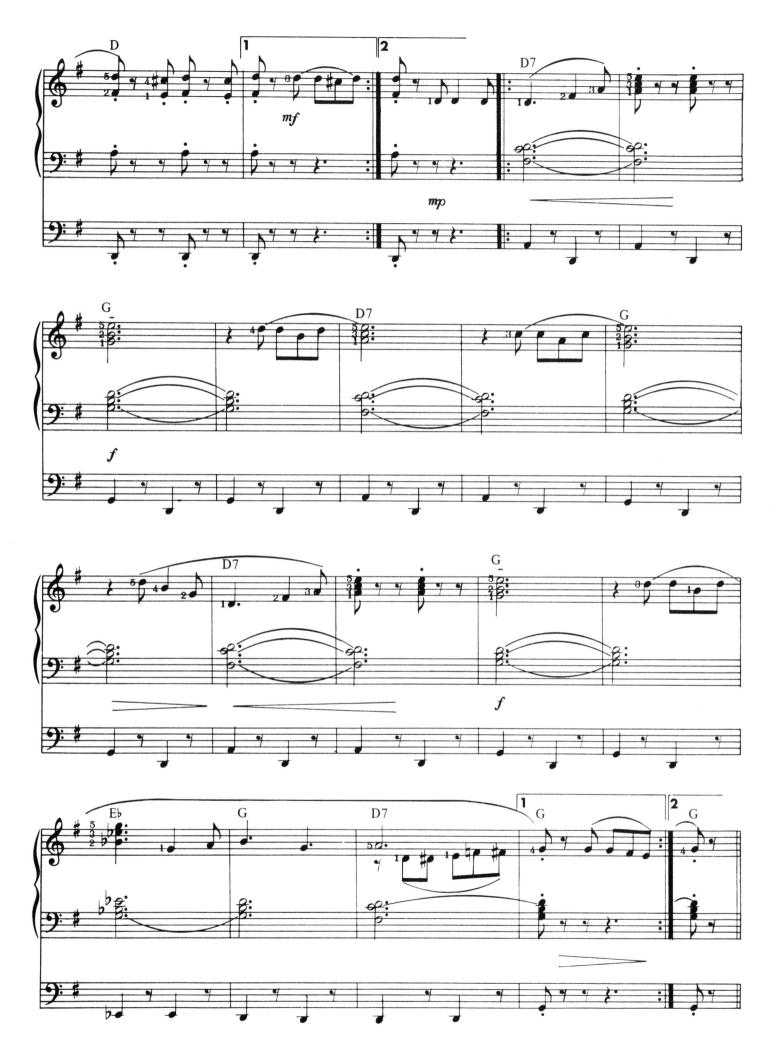

Drink To Me Only

Old English Air

Electronic Organs
Upper: Clarinet 8', Oboe 8'
Lower: Flute 8', 4'
Pedal: 8'
Vibrato: On

Drawbar Organs
Upper: 00 8757 234
Lower: (00) 7641 100 (0)
Pedal: 5 – (3)
Vibrato: On

With expression ♩. = 96

Drink to me on - ly with thine eyes And I will pledge with mine

Or leave a kiss with - in the cup And I'll not ask for wine. The

thirst that from the Soul doth rise, Doth ask a drink di - vine.

But might I of Jove's nec-tar sip I would not change for thine.

Were You There

Spiritual

Electronic Organs
Upper: Flute 8', Oboe 8'
Lower: Flute 8', String 8'
Pedal: 16' + 8'
Vibrato: On (Medium)

Drawbar Organs
Upper: 01 6475 320
Lower: (00) 6454 420 (0)
Pedal: 4 – (2)
Vibrato: On (Medium)

Slowly, with expression ♩ = 78

Lyrics:

Were you there when they cru-ci-fied my Lord? _____ Were you there when they cru-ci-fied my Lord? _____ Oh _____ Some-times it caus-es me to trem-ble, trem-ble, trem-ble, were you there when they cru-ci-fied my Lord? _____

Czardas

Monti

Electronic Organs
Upper: Violin (String) 8'
Lower: Flute 8', Diapason 8'
Pedal: 8'
Vibrato: On (Delay Optional)

Drawbar Organs
Upper: 00 5666 654
Lower: (00) 6543 000 (0)
Pedal: 4 – (3)
Vibrato: On (Delay Optional)

Skye Boat Song

Scottish Folk Song

Electronic Organs
Upper: Flute 8', Oboe 8'
Lower: String 8', Horn 8'
Pedal: 8'
Vibrato: On

Drawbar Organs
Upper: 01 6475 320
Lower: (00) 6454 420 (0)
Pedal: 4 – (2)
Vibrato: On

Swan Lake
(Theme)
Tchaikovsky

Electronic Organs		Drawbar Organs	
Upper:	Oboe 8′	Upper:	00 3660 200
Lower:	Flute 8′	Lower:	(00) 5302 000 (0)
Pedal:	16′	Pedal:	3 – (2)
Vibrato:	On (Medium)	Vibrato:	On (Medium)

On Wings Of Song

Mendelssohn

Electronic Organs		Drawbar Organs	
Upper:	Violin (String) 8'	Upper:	00 8222 232
Lower:	Flute 8'	Lower:	(00) 4302 000 (0)
Pedal:	8'	Pedal:	3 – (2)
Vibrato:	On	Vibrato:	On

On wings of song _ my treas - ure, we'll start our voy-age from

here _____ where beau - ti - ful nat - ure gives pleas - ure And

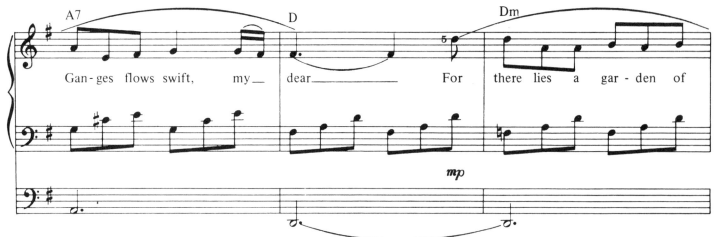

Gan - ges flows swift, my _ dear _____ For there lies a gar - den of

Blow The Wind Southerly

Sea Shanty

Electronic Organs
Upper: Flute 8'
Lower: Flute 8'
Pedal: 8'
Vibrato: On

Drawbar Organs
Upper: 00 8200 000
Lower: (00) 4302 000 (0)
Pedal: 3 – (2)
Vibrato: On

First Symphony
(Theme)
Brahms

Electronic Organs		Drawbar Organs	
Upper:	Synthesized Strings (Or Cello 16', Violin 8')	Upper:	40 8757 234
Lower:	Synthesized Strings (Or Flute 8', 4')	Lower:	(00) 7665 211 (0)
Pedal:	16' + 8'	Pedal:	6 – (3)
Vibrato:	On	Vibrato:	On

Waltz
(from 'Naila')
Delibes

Electronic Organs
Upper: Flute 8', 4'
Lower: Flute 8', String 8'
Pedal: 8'
Vibrato: On

Drawbar Organs
Upper: 00 7510 000
Lower: (00) 5443 211 (0)
Pedal: 4 – (2)
Vibrato: On

The Floral Dance

Old Cornish Air

Electronic Organs
Upper: Flute 16′, 8′, Trumpet 8′,
             String 8′
Lower: Flute 8′, 4′, String 8′
Pedal: 16′ + 8′
Vibrato: On

Drawbar Organs
Upper: 50 7600 302

Lower: (00) 3435 130 (0)
Pedal: 5 – (3)
Vibrato: On

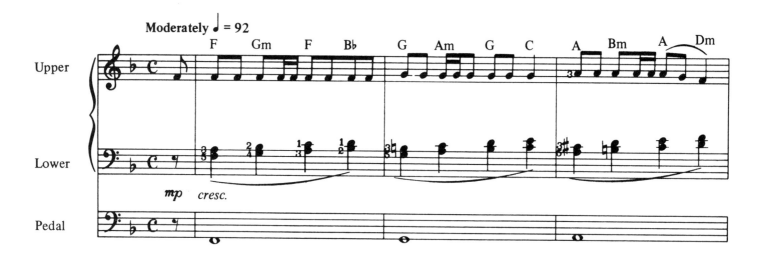

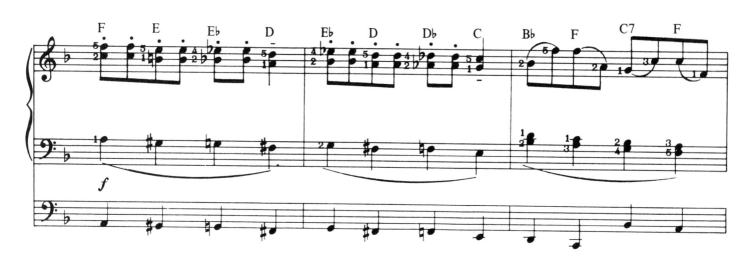

Kumbaya

Spiritual

Electronic Organs
Upper: Flute 8', 4', Saxophone 8'
Lower: Flute 8', String 8'
Pedal: 16' + 8'
Vibrato: On

Drawbar Organs
Upper: 00 7865 343
Lower: (00) 5653 120 (0)
Pedal: 5 – (3)
Vibrato: On

(Repeat & Fade ad lib.)

Quartette
(from 'Rigoletto')
Verdi

Electronic Organs
Upper: Flute 16', 8', String 8'
Lower: Flute 8', Diapason 8'
Pedal: 16' + 8'
Vibrato: On

Drawbar Organs
Upper: 40 5823 401
Lower: (00) 5004 121 (0)
Pedal: 5 – (2)
Vibrato: On

Tango

Albeniz

Electronic Organs		Drawbar Organs	
Upper:	Accordion (or Flute 16′, 8′, Trumpet 8′)	Upper:	00 8867 420
Lower:	Flute 8′, 4′	Lower:	(00) 5655 330 (0)
Pedal:	8′	Pedal:	5 – (3)
Vibrato:	Off (with Accordion) On (with Flutes, etc.)	Vibrato:	On

Shenandoah
Sea Shanty

Electronic Organs
Upper: Horn 8' (or Reed 8')
Lower: String 8'
Pedal: 8'
Vibrato: Off (with Horn);
           On (with Reed)

Drawbar Organs
Upper: 01 6475 320
Lower: (00) 6454 420 (0)
Pedal: 4 – (2)
Vibrato: On

Sonata Pathetique
(Theme)
Beethoven

Electronic Organs
Upper: Piano (or Flute 8')
Lower: Synthesized Strings (or
               String 8')
Pedal: 8'
Vibrato: Off (with Piano)
               On (with Flute)

Drawbar Organs
Upper: 00 8400 000
Lower: (00) 4333 111 (0)

Pedal: 4 – (2)
Vibrato: On

Romeo And Juliet
(Theme)
Tchaikovsky

Electronic Organs
Upper: Synthesized Strings (or
               Cello 16', Violin 8')
Lower: Flute 8', 4', String 8'
Pedal.   16' + 8'
Vibrato: On

Drawbar Organs
Upper: 40 8757 234

Lower: (00) 7655 211 (0)
Pedal: 6 – (3)
Vibrato: On

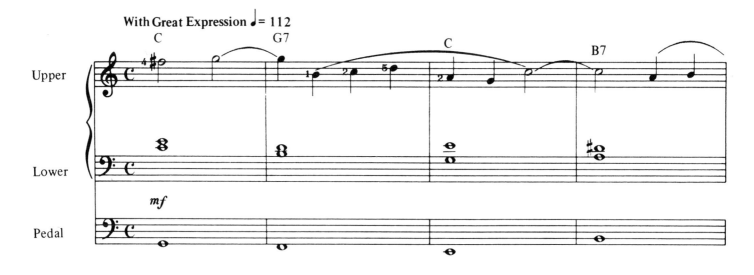

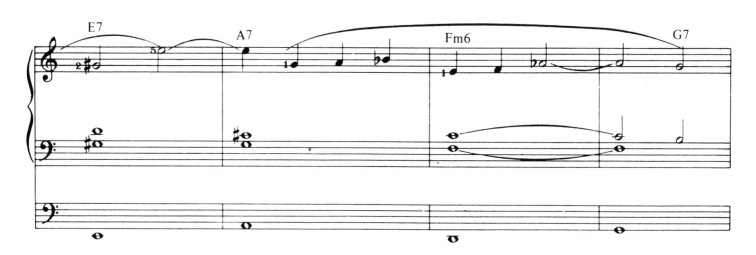

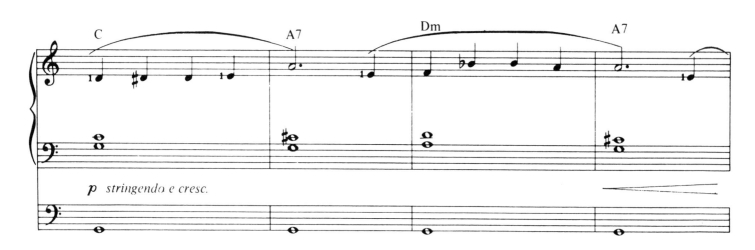

Rondeau
(from 'Abdelazer')
Purcell

Electronic Organs
Upper: Trombone 16', Trumpet 8'
Lower: Flute 8', 4', String 8'
Pedal: 16' + 8'
Vibrato: On

Drawbar Organs
Upper: 60 6520 753
Lower: (00) 5787 000 (0)
Pedal: 5 – (3)
Vibrato: On

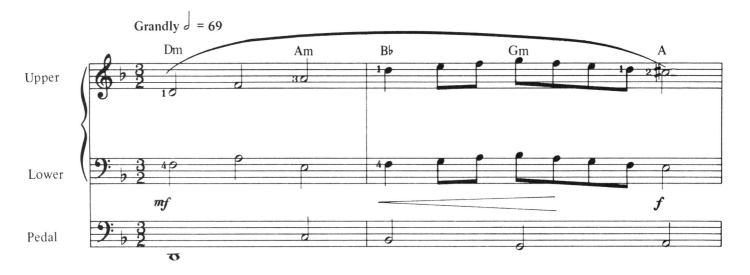

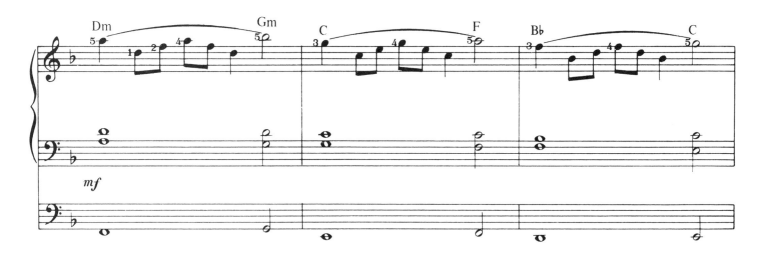

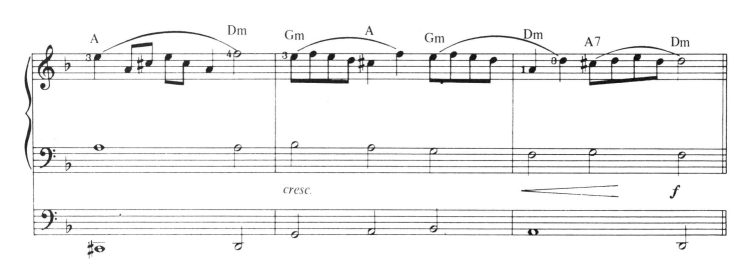

Beautiful Dreamer

Foster

Electronic Organs
Upper: Trombone 16'
Lower: Flute 8', String 8'
Pedal: 16' + 8'
Vibrato: On

Drawbar Organs
Upper: 60 6520 000
Lower: (00) 5753 000 (0)
Pedal: 5 – (3)
Vibrato: On

Song Of India

Rimsky-Korsakov

Electronic Organs		Drawbar Organs	
Upper:	Oboe 8'	Upper:	00 3660 200
Lower:	Synthesized Strings (or String 8')	Lower:	(00) 5543 000 (0)
Pedal:	8'	Pedal:	4 – (2)
Vibrato:	On (Mcdium)	Vibrato:	On (Medium)

Slowly ♩ = 72

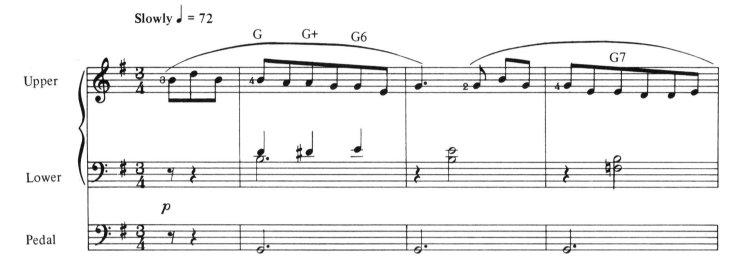

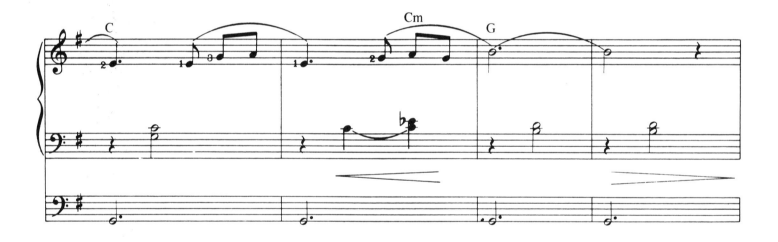

Scarborough Fair

Traditional

Electronic Organs		Drawbar Organs	
Upper:	Clarinet 8'	Upper:	00 7272 420
Lower:	String 8'	Lower:	(00) 5543 211 (0)
Pedal:	8'	Pedal:	4 – (2)
Vibrato:	On	Vibrato:	On

Peter And The Wolf
(Themes)
Prokofiev

Electronic Organs
Upper: Flute 8'
Lower: Flute 8', 4'
Pedal: 8'
Vibrato: On

Drawbar Organs
Upper: 00 8400 000
Lower: (00) 4302 000 (0)
Pedal: 3 – (2)
Vibrato: On

Meditation
(from 'Thaïs')
Massenet

Electronic Organs
Upper: Cello 16'
Lower: Flute 8', 4'
Pedal: 16' + 8'
Vibrato: On (Delay optional)

Drawbar Organs
Upper: 40 5545 330
Lower: (00) 6343 000 (0)
Pedal: 4 – (2)
Vibrato: On (Delay optional)

Reverie

Debussy

Electronic Organs
Upper: Oboe 8'
Lower: Flute 8'
Pedal: 16'
Vibrato: On (Medium)

Drawbar Organs
Upper: 00 3660 200
Lower: (00) 5302 000 (0)
Pedal: 3 – (2)
Vibrato: On (Medium)

La Cucaracha

Traditional

Electronic Organs
Upper: Trumpet 8'
Lower: Flute 8', 4'
Pedal: 8'
Vibrato: On

Drawbar Organs
Upper: 00 7677 540
Lower: (00) 5431 210 (0)
Pedal: 4 – (3)
Vibrato: On

Symphony No. 40
(Theme)
Mozart

Electronic Organs		Drawbar Organs	
Upper:	Synthesized Strings (or Cello 16′, String 8′)	Upper:	40 8757 234
Lower:	Flute 8′, 4′	Lower:	(00) 8665 000 (0)
Pedal:	8′	Pedal:	3 – (5)
Vibrato:	On	Vibrato:	On

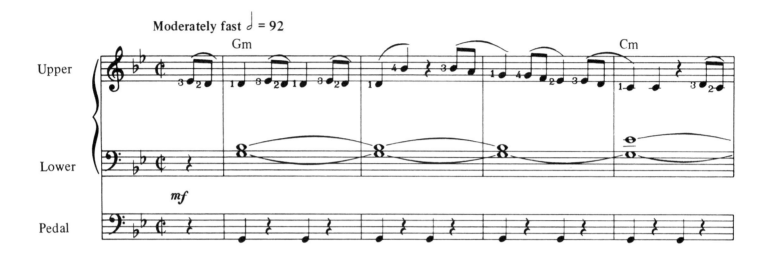

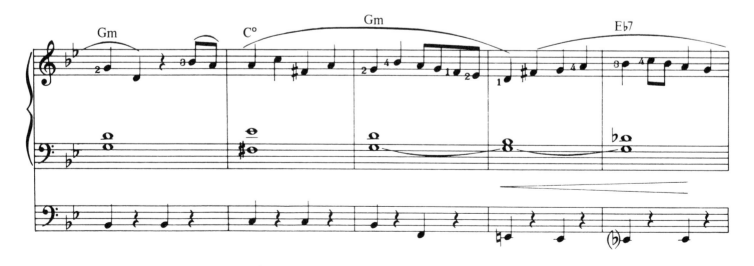

The Lark In The Clear Air

Irish Air

Electronic Organs
Upper: Flute 8'
Lower: String 8'
Pedal: 8'
Vibrato: On

Drawbar Organs
Upper: 00 8400 000
Lower: (00) 4233 111 (0)
Pedal: 4 – (2)
Vibrato: On

Dear_ thoughts are in _ my _ mind and _ my soul soars _ en - chant-ed. As I

hear the sweet _ lark _ sing in _ the clear _ air of the day. For a

ten - der beam-ing _ smile to my hope _ has _ been _ grant - ed. And to

mor - row she _ shall _ hear all _ my fond _ heart would _ say.

The Harmonious Blacksmith

Handel

Electronic Organs
Upper: Harpsichord (or Trumpet 8')
Lower: String 8', 4'
Pedal: 16' + 8'
Vibrato: Off

Drawbar Organs
Upper: 00 7677 540
Lower: (00) 5433 222 (0)
Pedal: 4 – (3)
Vibrato: Off

Light Cavalry

Suppe

Electronic Organs
Upper: Flute 8', 4', Trumpet 8', Glock.
Lower: Flute 8', 4'
Pedal: 16' + 8'
Vibrato: On

Drawbar Organs
Upper: 30 6846 234 + Glock.
Lower: (00) 6655 432 (0)
Pedal: 5 – (3)
Vibrato: On

To Coda ⊕

D.%. al Coda   ⊕ *CODA*

Roses From The South

Strauss Jnr.

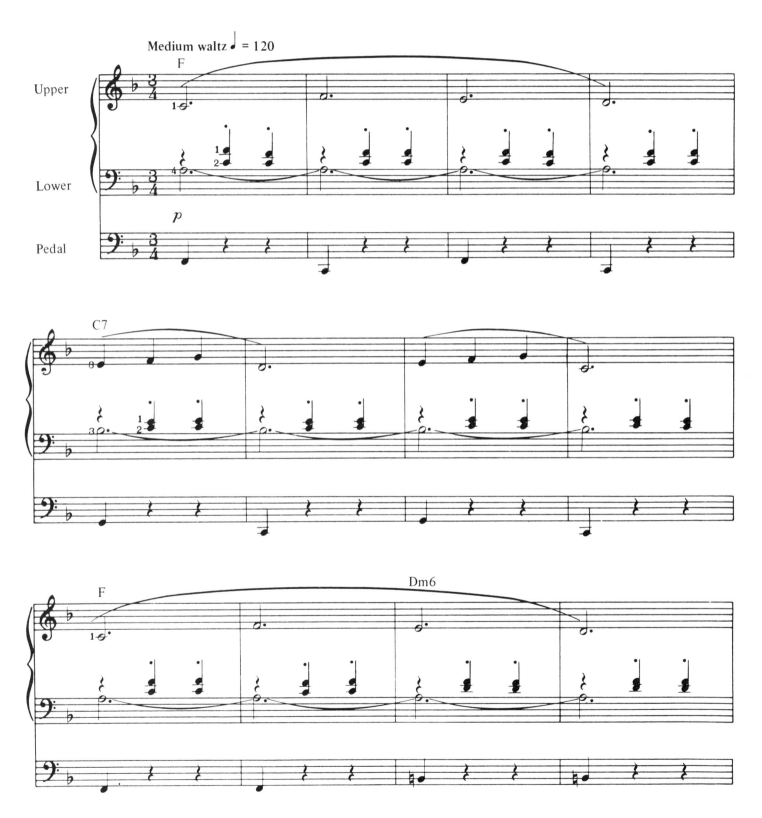

Serenade

Haydn

Electronic Organs		Drawbar Organs	
Upper:	Synthesized Strings (or Cello 16′, Violin 8′)	Upper:	40 8757 234
Lower:	Synthesized Strings (or Flute 8′, 4′)	Lower:	(00) 7665 211 (0)
Pedal:	16′ + 8′	Pedal:	6 – (3)
Vibrato:	On	Vibrato:	On

The Irish Washerwoman

Irish Jig

Electronic Organs
Upper: Violin (String) 8′
Lower: Flute 8′, 4′
Pedal: 8′
Vibrato: On

Drawbar Organs
Upper: 00 8222 232
Lower: (00) 4302 000 (0)
Pedal: 3 – (2)
Vibrato: On

Ah! So Pure
(from 'Martha')

Flotow

Electronic Organs
Upper: Flute 8′
Lower: String 8′
Pedal: 8′
Vibrato: On

Drawbar Organs
Upper: 00 8400 000
Lower: (00) 4233 111 (0)
Pedal: 4 – (2)
Vibrato: On

aim, ere she came, Dark the fu-ture seem'd to loom, Till her clear bril-liant sphere new with

light dis-pell'd the gloom. Woe! she fled: quick-ly sped all my joy in fleet-ing gleams; as I

wake, Hopes for-sake, Rob-bing me of god-like dreams, of god-like

rall e dim. _____

dreams. _____

_____ vine _____ she be-guil'd this heart of mine.

D.C. al Coda

✛ *CODA*

Pirate Chorus
(from 'The Pirates Of Penzance')
Gilbert and Sullivan

Electronic Organs
Upper: Flute 16′, 8′, 4′, String 8
Lower: Flute 8′, 4′
Pedal: 16′ + 8′
Vibrato: On

Drawbar Organs
Upper: 60 8856 364
Lower: (00) 6523 454 (0)
Pedal: 6 – (4)
Vibrato: On

plough the sea, Truce to nav - i - ga - tion, take an-oth - er sta - tion, let's va - ry

pi - ra - cee ___ with a lit - tle bur-gla - ree. With cat-like tread Up - on our

prey we steal In si - lence dread our caut-ious

way we feel!

The Swan

Saint-Saëns

Electronic Organs
Upper: Cello 16′
Lower: Flute 8′, 4′
Pedal: 16′ + 8′
Vibrato: On (Delay optional)

Drawbar Organs
Upper: 40 5545 330
Lower: (00) 6343 000 (0)
Pedal: 4 – (2)
Vibrato: On (Delay optional)

The House Of The Rising Sun

American Melody

Electronic Organs
Upper: Flute 16', 8', 4', 2'
Lower: Flute 8', String 8'
Pedal: 16' + 8'
Vibrato: On

Drawbar Organs
Upper: 88 8004 457
Lower: (00) 5554 044 (0)
Pedal: 6 – (3)
Vibrato: On

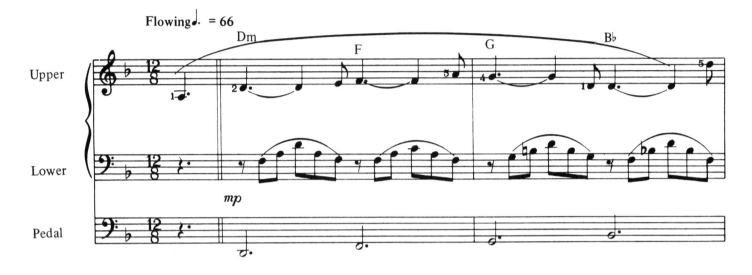

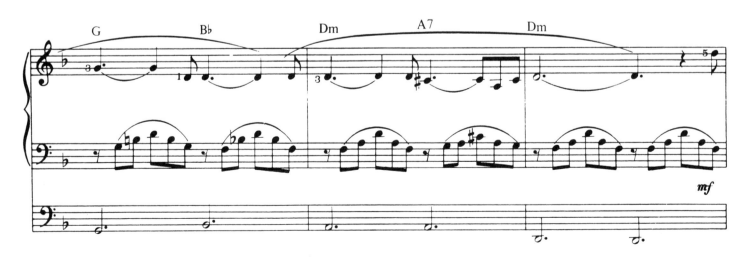

Fingal's Cave Overture (Themes)

Mendelssohn

Electronic Organs
Upper: Oboe 8′
Lower: String 8′, 4′
Pedal: 8′
Vibrato: On (Medium)

Drawbar Organs
Upper: 00 5786 400
Lower: (00) 5433 233 (0)
Pedal: 4 – (2)
Vibrato: On (Medium)

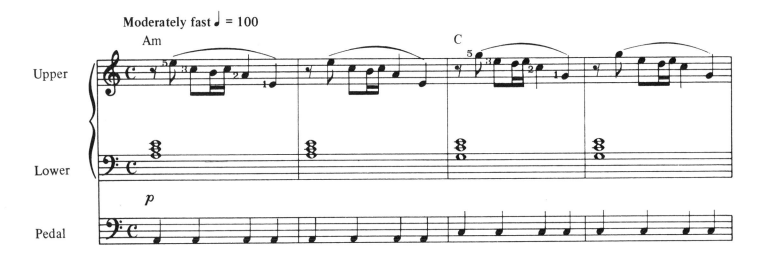

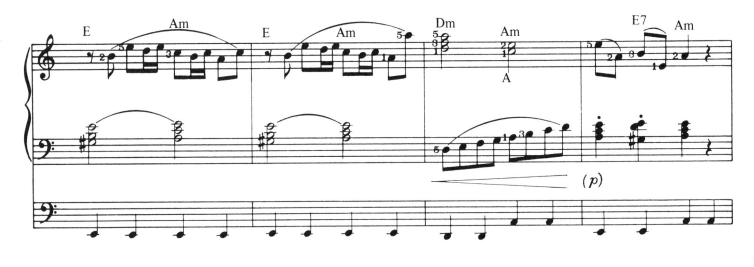

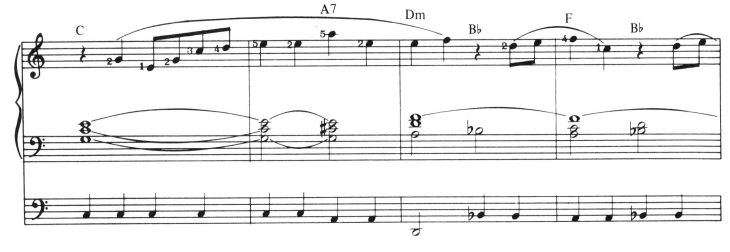

Crimond
(The Lord Is My Shepherd)
Traditional

Electronic Organs
Upper: Flute 8′, 4′
Lower: Diapason 8′ (or Flute 8′)
Pedal: 16′ + 8′
Vibrato: Off (Leslie: Chorale)

Drawbar Organs
Upper: 00 8600 000
Lower: (00) 5302 000 (0)
Pedal: 4 – (3)
Vibrato: Off (Leslie: Chorale)

With tranquillity ♩ = 80

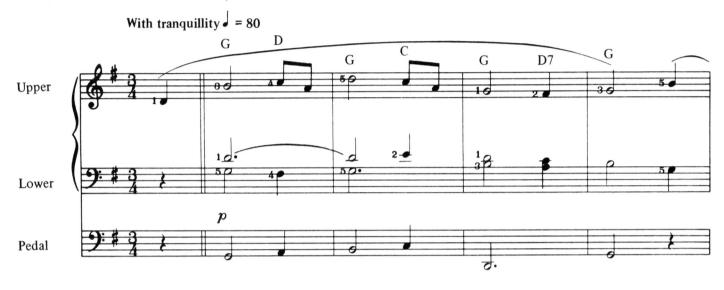

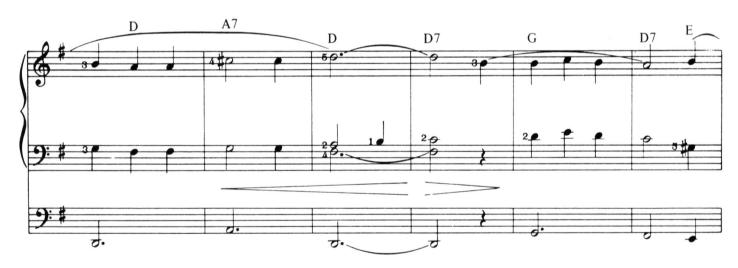

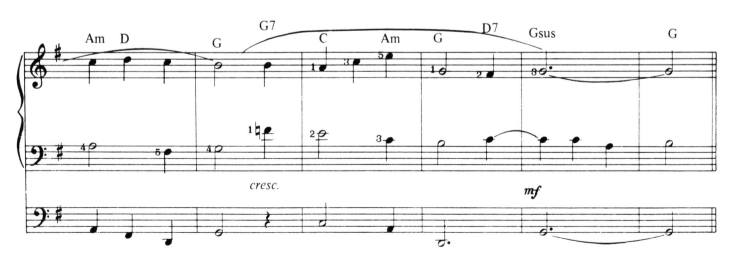

Mexican Hat Dance

Traditional

Electronic Organs
Upper: Flute 16′, 8′, 4′
Lower: Flute 8′, String 8′
Pedal: 16′ + 8′
Vibrato: On

Drawbar Organs
Upper: 80 0808 888
Lower: (00) 8854 000 (0)
Pedal: 5 – (3)
Vibrato: On

Where E'er You Walk

Handel

Electronic Organs
Upper: Oboe 8', Flute 8'
Lower: Flute 8', String 8'
Pedal: 16' + 8'
Vibrato: On

Drawbar Organs
Upper: 01 6475 321
Lower: (00) 5565 321 (0)
Pedal: 5 – (3)
Vibrato: On

La Cumparsita

Rodriguez

Electronic Organs
Upper: Accordion (or:
          Flute 16', 8', 4', Clarinet 8')
Lower: Flute 8', 4'
Pedal: 8'
Vibrato: Off (with Accordion)
          On (with Flutes and Clarinet)

Drawbar Organs
Upper: 54 8683 623

Lower: (00) 5654 332(0)
Pedal: 5 – (3)
Vibrato: On

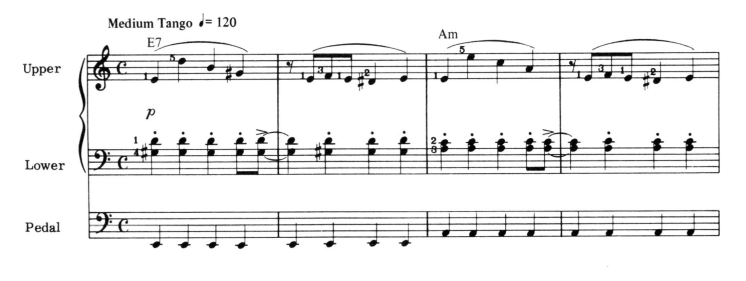

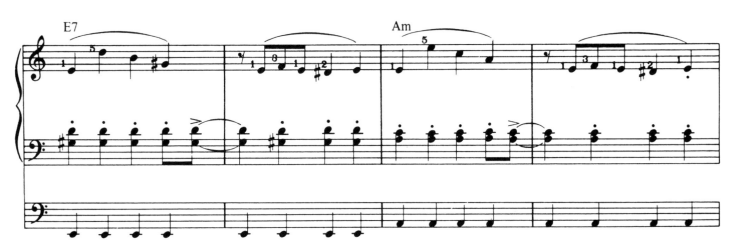

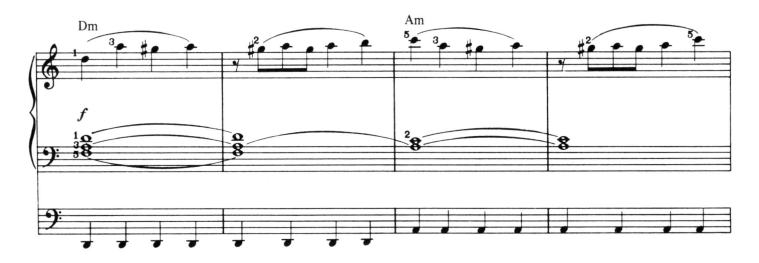

Who Is Sylvia

Schubert

Electronic Organs		Drawbar Organs	
Upper:	Trombone 16', Flute, 8',4'	Upper:	78 8515 000
Lower:	String 8', 4'	Lower:	(00) 5433 100 (0)
Pedal:	16' + 8'	Pedal:	5 – (3)
Vibrato:	On	Vibrato:	On

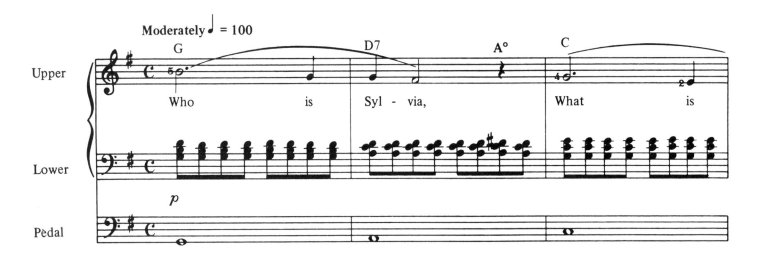

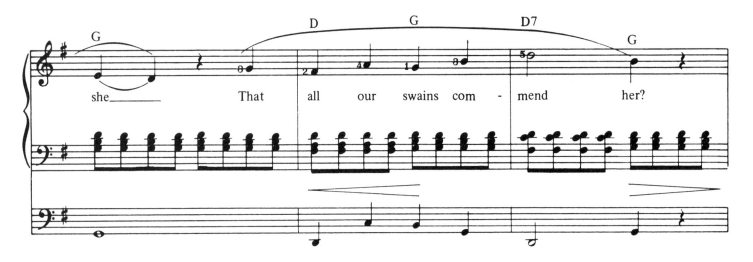

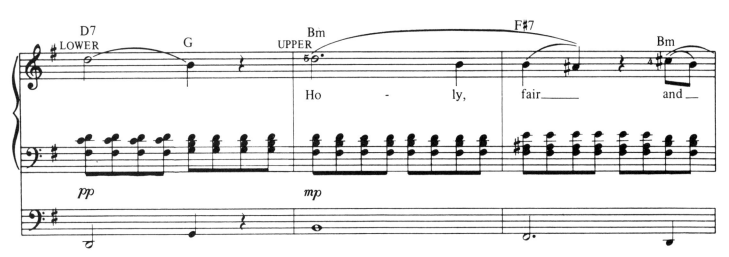

Maple Leaf Rag

Joplin

Electronic Organs
Upper: Piano (or Flute 16′, 8′, 4′, 2′)
Lower: Flute 8′, 4′, Diapason 8′
Pedal: 8′
Vibrato: Off (with Piano)
            On (with Flutes)

Drawbar Organs
Upper: 88 8000 008
Lower: (00) 8854 000 (0)
Pedal: 0 – (6)
Vibrato: On

Radetzky March

Strauss Snr.

Electronic Organs		Drawbar Organs	
Upper:	Flute 16', 8', 4'	Upper:	80 8606 004
Lower:	Flute 8', 4'	Lower:	(00) 6534 333 (0)
Pedal:	16' + 8'	Pedal:	5 – (3)
Vibrato:	On	Vibrato:	On

Largo
(from 'New World Symphony')
Dvořák

Electronic Organs
Upper: Oboe 8′
Lower: Synthesized Strings
         (or String 8′)
Pedal: 8′
Vibrato: On (Medium)

Drawbar Organs
Upper: 00 3660 200
Lower: (00) 5543 000 (0)

Pedal: 4 – (2)
Vibrato: On (Medium)

Theme

Paganini

Electronic Organs
Upper: Violin (String) 8'
Lower: Flute 8', 4'
Pedal: 8'
Vibrato: On

Drawbar Organs
Upper: 00 5666 654
Lower: (00) 6543 211 (0)
Pedal: 4 – (3)
Vibrato: On

Turkish Rondo

Mozart

Electronic Organs		Drawbar Organs	
Upper:	Piano (or Flute 16′ 8′, 4′)	Upper:	80 8606 004 + Piano
Lower:	Flute 8′, 4′	Lower:	(00) 6534 333 (0)
Pedal:	8′	Pedal:	5 – (3)
Vibrato:	Off (with Piano)	Vibrato:	On
	On (with Flutes)		

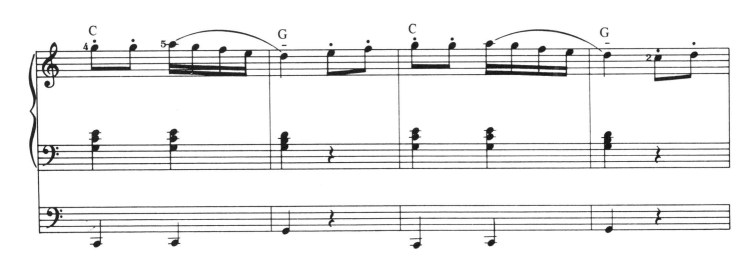

Soldiers' Chorus
(From 'Faust')
Gounod

Electronic Organs
Upper: Flute 16', 8', 4', 2', String 8'
Lower: Flute 8', 4', Diapason 8'
Pedal: 16' + 8'
Vibrato: On

Drawbar Organs
Upper: 82 8844 222
Lower: (00) 8463 640 (0)
Pedal: 5 – (5)
Vibrato: On

10774 11/90